THE COMPLETE
REVISION
WORKBOOK FOR
Writers

ARIELLE HAUGHEE

WRITER'S ATELIER BOOKS
WINTER PARK, FLORIDA

THE COMPLETE
REVISION
WORKBOOK FOR

Writers

TOOLS FOR A POLISHED NOVEL.

ARIELLE HAUGHEE

Published 2019 by Writer's Atelier, LLC

336 Grove Ave., Suite B

Winter Park, FL 32789

www.writersatelier.com

Cover design by Natalie Henry of Pretty Peacock Paperie

Book design by Inkstain Design Studio, LLC

Typeset editing by Battle Goddess Productions

Print Edition ISBN: 978-1-7336240-0-8

TABLE OF CONTENTS

1. Introduction

DEEP BREATHS, YOU GOT THIS

t's done. That draft that pulled out every ounce of willpower, drained every bit of sanity, is finally done.

Now what?

You know you need to clean it up. Maybe you've even peeked at it again, then slammed the laptop closed when you discovered the amount of work it needs and cried into the pillow your grandmother made. Just me?

Revision can be daunting, sometimes paralyzing if you have a messy draft.

Relax. Take a deep breath.

It's overwhelming to think about every single thing that needs to be done to clean up an entire book. The goal of this workbook is to make revision more manageable for you, no matter your experience or how many issues your draft has. Included here are tools to help you examine your work, figure out trouble spots, and fix any problems, renovating your story until it's HGTV worthy.

Every writer revises differently and each book will be a different process as well. Some manuscripts need more overhaul than others and like potty training, what worked for one may not work for the next. (Cue mom crying on the floor and eating all the M&Ms.) There are a lot of resources available here, but only use the tools that fit your project.

This is not a do-every-page-from-start-to-finish type of workbook. Use only what you need.

So crack those knuckles and let's get down to work!

Why Can Revision Take Forever?

Drafting is often the fun part of writing. You get to let go and write whatever you want, your muse twirling around in little ballerina circles inside your head. An event doesn't make sense in the plot? It's okay, I'll fix it *later*! Character doesn't have a clear motivation? No worries, I'll clean that up *later*, too! Let me just get all these amazing ideas down on the page and I will make everything perfect *later*.

Well, now it's *later*.

Revision is the real work in writing, unless you are one of those purple unicorns who writes a perfect first draft. Most of us have to roll up our sleeves and put in a lot of effort to get a story where it needs to be. I spend about 30% of my time drafting novels and 70% revising. Of course, this varies with each project. Several factors contribute to why revision often takes much longer than drafting.

There are two parts to revision: identifying problems and fixing them. The best tactic for noticing what needs to be fixed in your novel is getting perspective. You do that by stepping away for a little bit and letting time help you look at the story differently. Work on something else, whether it be a different part of this particular story or a short story/poem/flash fiction piece. You can then go back with fresh eyes and you'll be surprised at what you notice. Time is your friend.

Fixing the issues in your work is usually harder than figuring out what is wrong. You may notice your character is flat. What *exactly* do you do chapter after chapter to make them more round? After you've tried to fix something, how do you know it's really fixed? There is no easy answer for that, except to follow your **narrative instincts.** Writers often develop feelings about their story. If you hate, even despise, one part in particular in your work, it's your brain trying to tell you there's a problem. You just haven't figured it out yet. Follow your gut. If you sense something isn't right, then it probably isn't. And if you tried to fix a problem and still aren't sure, critique partners are the best tool for this. We'll discuss that more later. Figuring out how to fix a problem and determining if it is truly fixed also contributes to the time factor.

In addition, it's harder to measure progress in revision. With drafting, you can track your word count or see how far along you are in your storyline. Revision is a bit more nebulous and sometimes it can feel like you are working in circles, because sometimes you do. Therefore, it's harder to see the finish line.

All this time and hard work combined with not knowing if you are making any progress can lead to a very real problem: **revision burnout.** There is so much work to do, you just stop. You abandon your story, maybe even tell yourself you'll come back to it later. Giving up on your story is the biggest crime in writing. You spent all this time and energy on your project. Don't throw it all away. Yes, it's hard to fix a story. So, so hard. Don't quit because it's not easy. Many things can happen that will halt your revision process, some of them you won't be able to control, but others you can.

As you go through the revision process several times, you'll become aware of how you work as a writer, where you tend to linger, some of your bad habits, and good ones, too! You'll be able to revise faster with more practice. Keeping your motivation and having the right mindset makes a huge difference in your progress.

2. Mindset & Motivation

SEVEN REVISION DELAYS

You've finished drafting your great cat space opera, *Cosmic Catastrophe*, about Henrickson the wise-cracking Burmese who unwittingly finds himself in a galactic conspiracy to overthrow the evil Siamese rulers. He teams up with the beautiful, no-nonsense Persian, Libby, and together they search for the long-lost enchanted stones that will rid the galaxy of its suppressors once and for all. What they didn't expect to find was each other. Me-ow!

Phase one of your masterpiece is complete. Now time for phase two, revision. Let's look into some things that may halt the next part of your journey.

Delay #1: Planning Circles

Henrickson's backstory isn't quite complete and you need to figure it out to help explain his decision making. You decide he was abandoned in an alley as a kitten and that Osso, the lead evil Siamese, found him and injected him with a magical serum when he was little. Now you need to figure out all the kinds of magical serums they use in this world. And was Libby exposed to one at some point? What if all the characters were injected with serums? Now this will change the climax, so you need to redo that entire section. Now you decide to make another character, the wizard who created all the serums, and add in another POV…

You keep planning and planning, saying what you are going to do with your story without ever working on it. These are **planning circles.** One proposed change leads to another and another and yet another. It's an endless loop of changes. You spend so much time planning you either never get to the revision, or you never feel "ready" enough because there are more changes to make in your eyes.

Know when to stop making your revision plan and start doing the work of revising. Has it been weeks or months of planning? There will be things you decide to change as you go anyway, so get started.

Delay #2: Insecurity

You look over *Cosmic Catastrophe* and realize just how much work it needs. Libby is bossy and annoying whenever she talks. You have open plotlines with all her littermates you don't know how to close up. The pacing during the space battle is all off and the steamy scene afterward isn't so steamy. There are many more issues than you thought with this manuscript. You don't think you're skilled enough as a writer to fix the mess you've made.

The challenges of revision can pick away at your self-confidence and make you feel like you really can't do it, especially if you have a messy draft. Some of the story issues you'll have will take many rounds before you figure out how to fix them. It's frustrating and can make you feel like you're an idiot for not figuring it out. Or that you can't solve it at all and you have no idea what you're doing as a writer.

Start with one story issue. Take out a notebook and brainstorm all the possible fixes, even some unconventional ones. Something about handwriting your thoughts and ideas activates your brain and will remind you that you can do this. You had all the brilliance to come up with the story in the first place and that brilliance is still there for when it comes time to fix your story issues. Just look at one issue at a time, even if that means one scene. A little progress is still progress. Get your feet wet and you will get in a rhythm. And if you get overwhelmed and the insecurity stops your momentum, pull out that notebook again.

Delay #3: Fear

So what happens if you do spend all that time fixing everything with your cat space opera and it still isn't *good*? You may think you'll spend months, even years on a project that will be a total waste of time.

Writers at every level are thinking, "Is this good?" with each scene, each chapter, each book they work on. Fear can be helpful as long as it keeps you working on your story. When fear stops you from making any progress at all, then it's a real problem. Your story definitely won't be "good" if you stop or don't even start at all. Believe in your story and your abilities as a writer.

Delay #4: Hating Your Story

Libby and Henrickson are obnoxious pains in the butt. Osso is lame and you don't even like outer space anymore. That whole song and dance routine wouldn't work in a vacuum, you dummy!

You don't like Brussel sprouts, you despise pickled beets, but there is nothing you hate more than your story right now. It's stupid. Really, really stupid. At least that's what you think.

There is an emotional journey with stories that many writers feel. Here is a quick visual of the Writer's Emotional Roller Coaster of Revision.

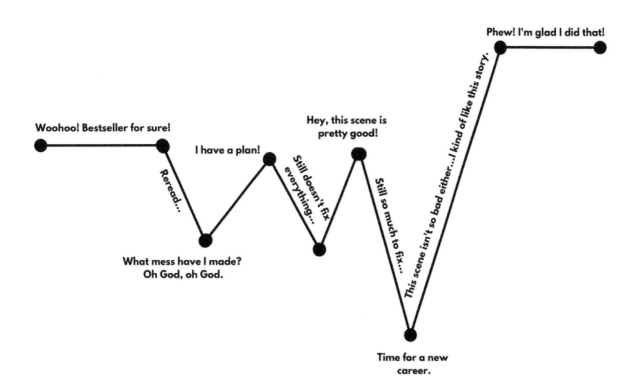

Hating your story is normal. I do many times throughout the process. Like with fear, use the negative emotion to fuel you to keep going. Don't stop entirely, you may just be in a downswing on the revision roller coaster.

Delay #5: Squirrel! AKA. Distractions

Your phone isn't the biggest distraction from your revision. While social media, email, and other digital nonsense can definitely suck up valuable time, the brightest, shiniest, most attention-getting thing for writers is a new idea.

Lightning strikes the brain and zaps an electrifying new story into your head. Now it itches. You NEED to work on this one.

Idea notebooks can help with lightning strikes. Jot down your story idea and all the exciting details, capturing the energy for when you can get to it. The great thing about idea notebooks is you can keep putting more and more ideas in there as they come, getting the energy out of your system until you can focus on it later.

But what if it's an amazing idea, just one, and you HAVE to do it now? Taking on another project while you are revising is possible, but you need to be careful it doesn't totally subsume your revision time. Consciously divide your time each week between revising and your new project, but be aware this will slow down the pace of your revision due to the simple fact that you will be spending less time on your first project.

What if you are already on a new project while revising and another idea comes to you? The more you divide your attention, the slower your progress will be on all your projects. This may lead to feeling like you work all the time but don't make much progress on anything.

Be very conscious of what projects get your active work time. Your goal is to finish one thing, not start many things.

Delay #6: Illusion

You've decided once and for all. *Cosmic Catastrophe* is way too much work. It would be much easier to start over with a new idea. You wouldn't have all the problems you have now because this next story would be better.

Riiiiiight.

You seem to have forgotten all that time you spent planning and all the twists and turns of drafting. And guess what, you'd still have to revise the next one! Yes, some stories are better than others. But you won't know until you finish. And every story you finish is an important step in your journey as an author.

Delay #7: Refreshing Time

The manuscript sat for a while and you are ready to dive back in. Hmmm, when did Henrickson steal the spacepod? Was that Tuesday? And what was that serum you planned for Osso? It's been too long since you've worked on it and you can't remember. Now you need to spend some time refreshing yourself on your story and your plan, delaying your final product further.

Every time you set your novel down and walk away from it for a while, you will have to spend valuable time remembering everything you wrote about. And the bigger the book, the longer it will take. Keep working on your manuscript every week, even if it is something small, to keep the story alive and active in your mind.

Keeping Your Motivation

Goal Setting, Routines, and Accountability

Set a realistic goal date for finishing your revision. Make a schedule for yourself that is aggressive but realistic. Time is your friend during revision because it gives you perspective. But it can become your enemy if you allow too much of it to pass. Be deliberate with your time and manage it well. Don't lose connection with your story. The more time passes between work sessions, the longer it will take for you to jump back into your story. Have an accountability system set in place. *See the Revision Goal Work Page* and *the Revision Timeline Work Page.*

Focus on Progress, not Perfection

Take the time to look at what you have done as you are revising, not on what still needs to be fixed or finished. Your goal is to make progress, not to make everything absolutely perfect. That's not even possible. When you have a challenging week or month or year, work a little bit on revising each week. Even if you only fit an hour in here and there, a little progress is still progress and it's more than what you had yesterday. Then when you have a chance, look back at everything you have done and be proud of your efforts.

Keep in Touch with Your Love of the Story

There will be many times when you want to quit and think this is all a waste of time. Remember why you started your story in the first place. What was that spark? That excitement? Write down a list of scenes or quotes from your book that you love. Keep your notebook out—the one where you frantically wrote down this lightning bolt of a story. Focus on the positive aspects and remind yourself that is what you are fighting for.

Build a Support Network

Connect with other writers and authors. In person is best but online works, too. We all know what it is like to be stuck in the mire of revision. Lean on your friends for support and talk through problems with them.

Revision

START DATE:

FINISH GOAL DATE:

Revision Timeline

MONTH:

GOAL:

Revision Timeline

MONTH:

GOAL:

3. The Complete Revision Workbook Overview

THE THREE FUNDAMENTALS OF THE REVISION PROCESS

Three activities happen during revision: evaluating, problem-solving, and planning. When you are just beginning revision, you'll have to do these three in order before you dive in. As the process is underway, you'll find new issues, come up with different fixes, and adapt your plan along the way. This workbook is set up to give resources for each of these processes in revision.

It took over a year to draft, but your mystery, *The Great Canine Caper,* is ready for revision.

To start, you need to **evaluate** your manuscript to determine where you have problems in your story. The best ways are to give yourself some distance to get perspective before you start and also to receive feedback from others. *The Evaluation Work Pages* and section eight, *Getting and Managing Feedback,* can assist with this process. You've gone through *The Great Canine Caper* and realized you didn't introduce the bad guy, well, bad girl, Roxy McFluffers, until the big climax at the doggie day spa. Oops.

Once you identify the issues you need to fix, it's time to **problem solve.** You can use the *Common Problems and Solution Ideas* in this workbook or refer to the *Resource Recommendation* section for more in-depth assistance. You realize you need to add a subplot where you bring Roxy in several times in the story, sabotaging all the dog shows you mentioned but never showed up in any scenes in the first draft.

After you've figured out how you are going to fix your issues, it's time to make a **plan** for execution. You'll need to figure out exactly what to do, chapter by chapter, to implement your solution ideas into your novel. You decide you'll introduce Roxy in chapter three where she'll set the fire sprinklers off and ruin the heroine's perfectly coiffed 'do before the show. Then in chapter six, she'll hit on the heroine's love interest, Spuds MacTENzie. And so on.

A word of caution—don't spend too much time planning before you get started or pausing to remake your plan. You may get caught in **planning circles** that distract you from making progress in your manuscript. There are issues you'll figure out how to address along the way. Once you get started, make sure you're always working on some part of the manuscript each week, even if it is tweaking a smaller part while you figure out an issue elsewhere.

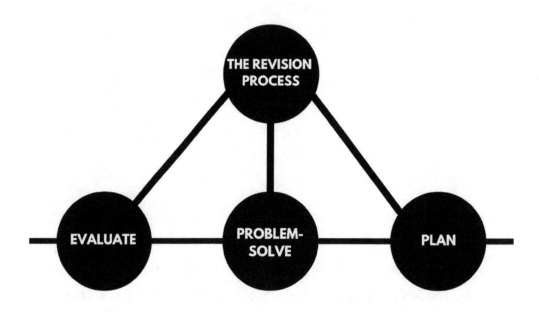

Revision Rounds as an Inverse Pyramid

We are house flippers, you and I. We have our own reality show called "Flipping Out," and we buy homes, fix them up, and sell them for ridiculous prices. I'm Alpha, the no-nonsense, get-this-done, gray coveralls person and you're Zedd, the one in the purple flannel shirt with all the zany, fun, creative ideas that make everything awesome. We're a good pair—it takes creativity and organization to get the job done. Just like writing.

On "Flipping Out," we take care of things in a specific order, tackling the big projects first and working our way down to the smaller ones. We replumb the house before putting in a new bathroom faucet. We replace the windows before hanging the curtains. We pull that hot tub out of the master bedroom before recarpeting. Why was that in there? Ew.

You can approach revision in the same way, taking care of the major issues with your story first, then working down to the small stuff. One of the main benefits of this approach is to save time. Revision can take what seems like forever, dragging on for years sometimes. Being efficient with your time and efforts will be less frustrating and help you avoid **revision burn-out**, a very real problem for writers. And of course, you'll have your book ready sooner if you stick to your plan.

I like to think of revision rounds as an inverse pyramid:

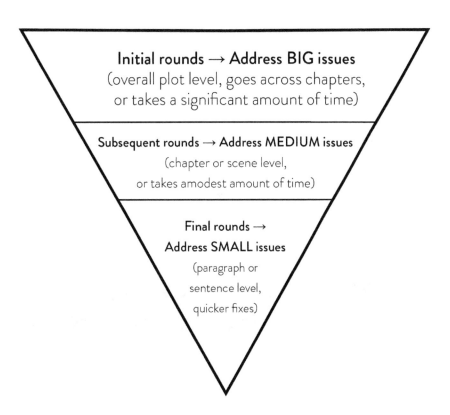

Initial rounds → Address BIG issues
(overall plot level, goes across chapters,
or takes a significant amount of time)

Subsequent rounds → Address MEDIUM issues
(chapter or scene level,
or takes amodest amount of time)

Final rounds →
Address SMALL issues
(paragraph or
sentence level,
quicker fixes)

The challenge is going to be keeping your focus and sticking to your plan. That doesn't mean not adapting your story as new ideas come to you, it means sticking to the big issues first and not being tempted to fix little things "along the way." It also means not spending hours on minutia you might eventually cut anyway.

Here's the rule: if you can fix it in under three seconds, then fine. So if you are reading your draft and notice a missing word or that an "S" needs to be added and you feel all twitchy about it, go ahead. But if you are doing this repeatedly when you are supposed to be addressing a larger issue, say changing a character's gender for example, then refocus and don't waste time changing all the en dashes to em dashes. Efficiency is key. Remember, we are trying to avoid revision burnout and going in circles.

This approach isn't ironclad, however. Sometimes when fixing a larger issue in a chapter, you can take care of a few smaller things as well. Revision rounds aren't always as clear and clean cut. The point is to focus your attention as best as possible during each round.

How many rounds will you need? That is going to depend on your book and it will change for every novel you write. Some stories come out messier than others. **Keep in mind that you can't fix everything in one round.** Focus on which layer you are improving and tell yourself you will get to whatever else in another round. This minimizes feeling overwhelmed because you're not trying to take care of everything at once.

How long will each round take? That also depends on your manuscript, as well as your self-discipline. You may have fewer big issues and more small issues or vice versa. If you aren't good about keeping to a routine and sticking to your schedule, it could take quite a long time for each round.

So stick to your routine and work on the big issues first, focusing your attention and energy the best you can.

Story Ingredients: What Every Novel Needs

What is the recipe for good fiction? Every book is different but they all have common underlying features that come together for a great story. It's a combination of character, setting, plot, and language.

CHARACTER	
COMPELLING CHARACTERS	• Authentic and realistic • Relatable for the reader • Likable or understandable • Mix of strengths and weaknesses/vulnerabilities
CLEAR MOTIVATIONS	• Everyone has a motivation that drives them • Main characters have a prominent, clear motivation shown at the beginning of the story • Motivations/Desires change at appropriate places as story unfolds
COMPLETED CHARACTER ARCS	• Characters change with story experience • Different at the end of the story

STORY PROBLEMS THAT ARE APPROPRIATE TO THEM	• Problems that are in direct contrast to their motivations • Problems that come from their setting or place in life, something connected to them
SOLID POINTS-OF-VIEW (POV)	• POV is clear and consistent throughout • With multiple POV, each one has a distinct perspective on the story

SETTING

CLEAR SETTINGS	• Large-scale such as country/city • Small-scale such as one room • Consistent details and locations
INTEGRATED SETTING	• Sensory details show totality of experience • Influences character background, types of problems—alive like a character
*CONSISTENT WORLDBUILDING (*FANTASY & SCIENCE FICTION)	• Well thought-out worldbuilding elements that are consistent and clear • Fantastical elements integrated organically and at the appropriate time in the story

PLOT

GREAT HOOK AND CLOSING LINE	• Opening hooks the reader • Closing line gives appropriate sense of completion
STORY BEGINS IN THE RIGHT PLACE	• Starts with the inciting event

INFORMATION GIVEN AT CORRECT PLACE	• Integrated into the story when appropriate
ORGANIC, CONNECTED PLOTLINE	• One event leads to the next and has a natural flow
CONFLICT IN MANY PLACES	• Within a character • Between characters • From the outside world • As much as possible!
PACING THAT BUILDS TOWARD CLIMAX	• Tension increases as story unfolds • More problems occur with progression of plot • Appropriate down times for reader to digest story
EXPLOSIVE, APPROPRIATE CLIMAX	• Worst possible scenario for character(s) • Highest tension and conflict
SATISFACTORY RESOLUTION(S)	• Solves most conflict • Related to main character's good qualities

LANGUAGE

ENGAGING VOICE	• Storytelling style has recognizable personality
EVOKES FEELINGS FROM THE READER	• Reader goes through an emotional journey along with the characters and storyline
CRISP, INTERESTING PROSE	• Clean, tight sentences and paragraphs • Descriptive elements engage the reader
ENGAGING DIALOGUE	• Moves the story forward • Sounds different for each character

OVERALL	
NARRATIVE BALANCE	• Narration and dialogue both present in appropriate amounts
CREATIVE AND UNIQUE CHARACTERISTICS	• Elements that make the story original and different

GETTING STARTED

Step #1: Air out the draft for six weeks

Work on something else, take a vacation, paint a mural of an epic battle between Chewbacca and the Care Bears—whatever you need to do to get a mental break from your story. The time away from your manuscript will give you much needed perspective as well as refresh your energy for the story. But don't let it go for too long. Set a revision start date and stick to it. See *The Revision Goal Work Page* and *The Revision Timeline Work Page* to help keep you on track.

Step #2: Read your draft from start to finish without making changes

That's right. Don't change anything, just read. Your goal here is to get an overall picture of the work that needs to be done. Remember you want to be efficient and tackle big problems first. So resist the urge to edit as you go. Ignore that twitch! As you are reading:

- If you haven't already, create a summary of what happens in each chapter. *Planning Page: Original Story Summary* is available for this.
- Take notes on *Planning Page: Rereading Review Notes* for each chapter and for things you notice overall in your work.

*All of the Planning Work Pages are in the back of this workbook for easy access as you are revising.

Step #3: Evaluate your work

Review the *Story Ingredients* table and look for areas where your work needs improvement. *The Evaluation Work Pages* are available to help you assess different areas of your story to discover any hidden problems. Remember to use only pages you need.

Step #4: Problem-solve

Once you have identified the issues in your manuscript, you can use the *Common Problems and Solution Ideas* and the *Problem-Solving Work Pages* to assist you in figuring out how to fix problems in your story.

Step #5: Make a Revision Plan

Use your *Rereading Review Notes*, your *Evaluation Work Pages*, and your *Problem-Solving Work Pages* to guide you in making your chapter-by-chapter *Revision Plan*. It may also be helpful to organize your issues biggest to smallest on the *Prioritizing Issues Work Page* so you know what to attack during the first rounds and can note that in your *Revision Plan*.

Step #6: Implement your plan and stick to your goal schedule

Time to work! Start at the beginning of your novel and work through the big issues in each chapter. Your Revision Plan may change as you go along and you discover new issues or better solutions. Stick to the schedule you made as best as possible and try to avoid the delays mentioned earlier.

Step #7: Subsequent Revision Rounds

Reread and reevaluate your work. Did you fix your big problems? Check if you need to problem-solve again. Then dive into the next round and tackle medium or smaller issues. Repeat this process as many times as it takes to polish your work.

Step #8: Get Feedback

During the later rounds, you will want to get feedback from critique partners, editors, and beta readers. See *Getting and Managing Feedback* for more information on finding reliable sources and evaluating feedback. Then problem-solve, plan, and execute to address the issues brought to your attention by outside readers.

Step #9: Keep at It

Don't be too hasty and send something out into the world, calling it "done," before it is truly ready. Writers can get itchy about wanting to "just be done with it." You don't want to spend all that time working on your book just to rush it out the door before making it as good as it can be. Take your time doing as many rounds of revision as the project needs.

Step #10: *Celebrate!*

You did it! You finally did it! Do whatever you enjoy the most to celebrate your hard work. Go out to a nice dinner, eat your favorite dessert, or do my personal favorite—take a very long, uninterrupted nap. You've earned it.

REVISION:

GETTING STARTED

1. AIR OUT YOUR DRAFT FOR 6 WEEKS

2. READ DRAFT START TO FINISH. DON'T STOP TO MAKE CHANGES

3: EVALUATE YOUR WORK

4. PROBLEM-SOLVE

5. MAKE A REVISION PLAN

6. IMPLEMENT YOUR PLAN + STICK TO YOUR GOAL SCHEDULE

7. SUBSEQUENT REVISION ROUNDS

8. GET FEEDBACK

9. KEEP AT IT

10. CELEBRATE!

4. Evaluation Work Pages

MAIN CHARACTER ARC

Character: _____

Initial Motivation/Goal: _____

_____

_____

Strengths: _____

_____

Deficiencies/Weaknesses: _____

_____

Impacting Events: _____

_____

New Motivation/Goal: _____

_____

Overall Change at Conclusion: _____

_____

_____

CHARACTER

SUPPORTING CHARACTERS

Character 1: _____

Motivation/Goal: _____

_____

Relevant Info: _____

_____

Unique Characteristics: _____

_____

Key Role in Story: _____

_____

Character 2: _____

Motivation/Goal: _____

_____

Relevant Info: _____

_____

Unique Characteristics: _____

_____

Key Role in Story: _____

_____

CHARACTER

BIG PLOT BOXES

Chap: _____

Tension Level: _____

Chap: _____

Tension Level: _____

Chap: _____

Tension Level: _____

Chap: _____

Tension Level: _____

Chap: _____

Tension Level: _____

Chap: _____

Tension Level: _____

PLOT

BIG PLOT BOXES

Chap: _____

Tension Level: _____

Chap: _____

Tension Level: _____

Chap: _____

Tension Level: _____

Chap: _____

Tension Level: _____

Chap: _____

Tension Level: _____

Chap: _____

Tension Level: _____

PLOT

BIG PLOT BOXES

Chap: _____

Tension Level: _____

Chap: _____

Tension Level: _____

Chap: _____

Tension Level: _____

Chap: _____

Tension Level: _____

Chap: _____

Tension Level: _____

Chap: _____

Tension Level: _____

PLOT

BIG PLOT BOXES

Chap: _____

Tension Level: _____

Chap: _____

Tension Level: _____

Chap: _____

Tension Level: _____

Chap: _____

Tension Level: _____

Chap: _____

Tension Level: _____

Chap: _____

Tension Level: _____

PLOT

BIG PLOT: THREE ACT OVERVIEW

ACT I

Set Up/Inciting Incident

ACT II

Confrontation

ACT III

Resolution

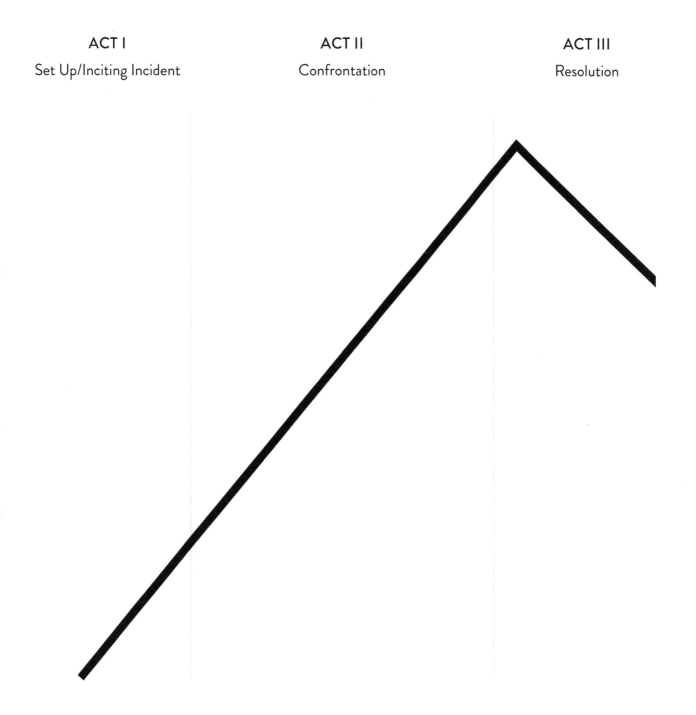

PLOT

BIG PLOT QUESTIONS

Is the story direction consistent with the opening ground work?

Is the story problem clear?

Does each major event flow naturally to the next?

Is there enough conflict?

PLOT

BIG PLOT QUESTIONS

Does the tension increase, culminating at the climax?

Is the climax the worst possible moment for the characters?

Does the solution match the story problem and make sense logically?

Does the conclusion give a satisfactory answer to the story problem presented?

PLOT

SUBPLOT EVALUATION

Subplot 1:

Brief Description:

Characters Involved:

Key Element(s) Contributed to Overall Plot:

Closed Up How and When:

PLOT

SUBPLOT EVALUATION

_____

Subplot 2:

_____

Brief Description:

_____

Characters Involved:

_____

Key Element(s) Contributed to Overall Plot:

_____

Closed Up How and When:

_____

PLOT

CHAPTER STRUCTURE

Chapter:

Is the opening interesting and a natural jump from the previous chapter?

Is there adequate attention to each event?

Does it flow with a beginning, middle, and end?

Does the pacing vary so readers have the excitement of conflict but also time to digest the narrative?

PLOT

CHAPTER STRUCTURE

Is each POV clear and easy to transition between?

Is there an appropriate ratio of narration to dialogue?

Does it end with a cliffhanger or natural pause?

Is there a sense of completion?

PLOT

SCENE EVALUATION

Scene Description:

Location in Story:

Characters Involved:

Conflict(s) Involved:

PLOT

SCENE EVALUATION

Parts Critical to Story Momentum:

Character Revealed:

Ratio of Narration to Dialogue:

PLOT

PROBLEM AND SOLUTION

STORY PROBLEMS	SOLUTION IDEAS	THE RIGHT PERSON WHO SOLVES?

PLOT

CAUSE AND EFFECT

CAUSE OF CHOICE / EVENT / ACTION	EFFECTS	LOGICALLY CONNECTED?

PLOT

SETTING EVALUATION

Setting:

Sensory Details:

Feeling of the setting for the characters: Shown in which details?

How characters interact with setting:

Any missing details or inconsistencies?

Is this the appropriate setting for the event(s) to take place?

SETTING

ESSENTIAL INFORMATION

Information:

Does it reveal character? If so, how?

Does it move the plot forward? If so, how?

Does it contribute to theme or tone? If so, how?

Is it integral to understanding the setting? If so, how?

ESSENTIALS

ESSENTIAL INFORMATION

How would the story be affected if this information was cut out?

Remember, something may be beautiful or funny or a part you really enjoyed writing, but if you answered no to the four questions, it should be cut.

5. Common Problems & Solution Ideas

T he following section is an extensive list of common issues writers have in their stories. Some of these issues are more significant problems than others so you will have to determine if they are a big, medium, or small issue in reference to your own work. They are organized by category: characters, plot, setting, and language.

Solution ideas are given and correlating *Problem-solving Work Pages* to help you work through issues. Many of these topics, such as POV and showing instead of telling, can be studied in greater depth for a better understanding. Please refer to the *Resource Recommendations* section for where to find more information on many of these topics.

COMMON PROBLEM & SOLUTION IDEAS

CHARACTER

PROBLEM	DESCRIPTION	SOLUTION IDEAS
UNLIKABLE CHARACTER	The character is too whiny, too aggressive, too cold...and the reader is not rooting for them.	• Give the character a vulner-ability people can relate to. • Clarify and strengthen their motivation. • Adjust their dialogue/how they speak to others. • Include more inner thoughts and rationale for choices. • Give them a pet/someone vulnerable they care for. • Show them helping others. *Evaluation Pages: Main Character Arc, Supporting Character* *Problem-solving Page: Fleshing Out a Character, Changing a Character*

PROBLEM	DESCRIPTION	SOLUTION IDEAS
STEREOTYPICAL CHARACTER	The character is an overdone archetype like the nagging mother or the dumb jock. The character is a common misconception/inaccurate representation for someone of a certain ethnicity, gender, sexual orientation...	• Give the character a unique characteristic or a twist on the usual version. • Deepen the character with specific strengths, weaknesses, and vulnerabilities. • Research ethnic/gender/ orientation stereotypes. • Use a sensitivity reader. *Evaluation Pages: Main Character Arc, Supporting Character Problem-solving Page: Fleshing Out a Character, Changing a Character*
FLAT OR BORING CHARACTER	The character is...well...meh. The reader doesn't feel a connection or doesn't care if they achieve their goal.	• Give the character a unique characteristic. • Give the character a vulnerability people can relate to. • Clarify and strengthen their motivation. • Include more inner thoughts and rationale for choices. *Evaluation Page: Supporting Characters, Main Character Arc Problem-solving Page: Fleshing Out a Character, Changing a Character*

PROBLEM	DESCRIPTION	SOLUTION IDEAS
UNCLEAR ANTAGONIST	The reader is unsure who the "bad guy" is and not in a "whodunit" kind of way. There is no antagonist in the story where one is intended/needed for the plot.	• Identify/develop the antagonist and flesh out their character. • Integrate them in more scenes/add more subplot. • Examine their actions and determine how they can use their bad strengths to challenge the main characters. *Evaluation Page: Supporting Character* *Problem-solving Page: Fleshing Out a Character, Changing a Character, Adding a Subplot*
WEAK ANTAGONIST	The "bad guy" isn't that bad. The "bad guy" isn't involved much in the story.	• Flesh out the antagonist and give them strengths that match the main character's weaknesses. • Have them create the worst possible scenarios for the main characters. • Integrate them in more scenes/add more subplot. *Evaluation Page: Supporting Character* *Problem-solving Page: Fleshing Out a Character, Changing a Character, Adding a Subplot*

PROBLEM	DESCRIPTION	SOLUTION IDEAS
UNCLEAR GOAL OR MOTIVATION	It's unclear what the character wants as they are going through the story. What they want doesn't change appropriately as the story unfolds.	• Establish motivation early on in the story and revisit during key events. • Identify key turning point in the story where the goal changes and add character's thoughts/ narration showing the change. *Evaluation Page:* *Main Character Arc* *Problem-solving Page:* *Fleshing Out a Character*
LACKS FULL CHARACTER ARC	The character does not undergo a change or learn anything at the end of the story.	• Examine initial motivation and determine if/when it changes. • Identify events that cause character to confront previous beliefs. • Include narrative reflection after key events, particularly the climax. *Evaluation Page:* *Main Character Arc*

PROBLEM	DESCRIPTION	SOLUTION IDEAS
POV UNCLEAR	The reader doesn't know who is telling the story.	• Identify who should be telling the story for each chapter/section. • Integrate that character's thoughts, reactions, and perspective into the narration. *Problem-solving Page:* *Clearing Up POV* *Planning Page:* *Updated Story Summary*
POV HOPS AROUND	The POV jumps from character to character and is confusing for the reader. The POV shifts between characters without a clear transition.	• Identify who should be telling the story for each chapter/section. • Remove any other character's thoughts, internal reactions, or perspective from the narration. • Create a clear transition between POV changes by using section breaks or labeling sections with the character name. *Problem-solving Page:* *Clearing Up POV* *Planning Page:* *Updated Story Summary*

PROBLEM	DESCRIPTION	SOLUTION IDEAS
LACKS REACTIONS	The character shows little or no emotion as they go through the events of the story.	• Develop a list of how the character acts when they are angry, sad, happy, etc. • Identify places in the story where the character would have an emotional reaction to the events. • Incorporate the appropriate verbal reactions, physical reactions, and thoughts in the appropriate places in the story. *Problem-solving Page: Fleshing Out a Character, Language Use*
TOO MANY REACTIONS	The character has so many emotions or physical reactions they seem like a soap opera star or a cartoon.	• Do a scene study: count how many physical reactions (hand on waist, stomping, etc.) the character has and cut half, then see if the emotion of the scene is still there. • Make emotional reactions more subtle by decreasing character thoughts and inner reflection. *Problem-solving Page: Language Use*

PROBLEM	DESCRIPTION	SOLUTION IDEAS
EMOTIONAL GROWTH BETWEEN CHARACTERS NOT FULLY DEVELOPED	The friendship, familial relationship, or romantic relationship does not change as the story progresses. The relationship goes from flat to a seemingly sudden change with no interim progress.	• Identify key points in the plot that draw the characters together and ones that push them apart. • Include character thoughts and emotional reactions at key points to show the growing/changing relationship. *Genre Page: Romance (can use for nonromantic relationships)*
KEY CHARACTERS NEED MORE FACE TIME	A character with an important role seemingly pops out of nowhere to do their part. An important character disappears for a large part of the book to reemerge later.	• Track which chapters/scenes the character is in. • Integrate the character in appropriate places in the story. *Genre Page: Mystery (treat character like a "clue" to be introduced)*
NAME DOESN'T FIT	The brutal mob boss named Stanley H. McCorkle isn't quite cutting it.	• Research names of real people who match your character, then adapt. • Research genre specific names. • Use a name that matches their personality or is ironic, such as a rogue priest named Creed.

PROBLEM	DESCRIPTION	SOLUTION IDEAS
TOO MANY CHARACTERS	You could fill Ben Hill Griffin Stadium with all the characters named in your story.	• Identify which characters have key contributions to the plot. • Cut nonessential characters. • Find characters that can be merged/roles subsumed by other characters. *Evaluation Page: Supporting Characters* *Problem-solving Pages: Cutting a Character, Merging Characters*
SIMILAR NAMES	Names are too similar and are easy to confuse such as Derek and Erik or Sharon and Shirley.	• Keep a list of all character names. • Identify similar names and adjust as needed.

COMMON PROBLEM & SOLUTION IDEAS

PLOT

PROBLEM	DESCRIPTION	SOLUTION IDEAS
SLOW BEGINNING/ STORY DOESN'T START IN RIGHT PLACE	Readers have a hard time getting into the story or are bored with the opening.	• Identify inciting incident and start as close as possible to the event. • Integrate backstory in snippets as the story progresses. • Introduce conflict of some kind immediately. • Balance narration and dialogue. *Evaluation Page: Big Plot Pages, Essential Information Problem-solving Pages: Adding Conflict, Cutting a Scene, Merging Scenes*
CONFUSING BEGINNING	Readers have no idea what's going on.	• Ground the reader in the scene more with a few setting details and a little more character info. • Start with another scene if the opening has too much action or dialogue. • Starting with dreams or flashbacks are often confusing for readers.

PROBLEM	DESCRIPTION	SOLUTION IDEAS
INFO DUMP	The character's or world's whole backstory is presented in detail in large chunks.	• Decide which details are essential to understanding the story and only include those. • Distribute pieces of information as the reader needs it in the story. *Evaluation Page: Essential Information* *Problem-solving Page: Cleaning Up/Clarifying Backstory* *Genre Page: Historical, Fantasy Worldbuilding*
INFORMATION NOT GIVEN AT CORRECT TIME	The reader learns about backstory/ worldbuilding too soon or too late in the story.	• Determine the key points in the story where the reader needs the information. • Give the information as clues along the way. *Problem-solving Page: Cleaning Up/Clarifying Backstory Genre Page: Fantasy Worldbuilding, Mystery*
BACKSTORY UNDERDEVELOPED	Events occurring before the storyline are unclear, causing reader confusion.	• Flesh out the backstory. • Integrate parts that are necessary to reader understanding. *Problem-solving Page: Cleaning Up/Clarifying Backstory Genre Page: Fantasy Worldbuilding*

PROBLEM	DESCRIPTION	SOLUTION IDEAS
THE STORY DIRECTION ISN'T FOLLOWED	The groundwork is laid for the story to be about one thing, but it veers off and is about another.	• Restructure the opening of the story to match later events. • Realign the direction of the story to match the beginning and rework the story events. *Evaluation Page: Big Plot Pages* *Problem-solving Pages: Cutting a Subplot, Adding a Subplot*
STORY PROBLEM IS UNCLEAR	The direction of the story isn't laid out and the plot seems to meander.	• Write a logline or one sentence that boils your story down to its most basic components. • Identify the main problem of the story, not the premise. • Make sure all events link to the main problem. • Integrate narration focused on character thoughts and reactions to the main problem. *Evaluation Page: Big Plot Pages*

PROBLEM	DESCRIPTION	SOLUTION IDEAS
MISSING SENSE OF URGENCY	The story moves forward at a slower pace and there is no lurking danger.	• Identify and integrate a pressing consequence if the character does not do something. • Integrate the character thinking about the consequence and the anxiety or pressure they feel. *Problem-solving Pages: Adding Conflict, Adding a Subplot, Adding a Scene, Fleshing Out Characters* *Genre Page: Thriller/Horror*
CHARACTER MEETS GOALS TO EASILY	Presto! Problem solved quickly and easily.	• Integrate the try-fail, try-fail, try-succeed structure. • Identify character's weaknesses and give challenges in line with those weaknesses. *Problem-solving Pages: Fleshing Out a Character, Adding Conflict, Adding a Subplot, Adding a Scene*
TOO MANY ASIDES/ INTROSPECTION SLOWS PACING	The character loves to share funny stories about their childhood or lament their station in life over and over and over. They share too much and take away from the plot.	• Determine if the information is essential to the story and trim as necessary. *Evaluation Page: Essential Information*

PROBLEM	DESCRIPTION	SOLUTION IDEAS
FLASHBACKS INTERRUPT PACING	A long flashback halts the pacing of the story in the present. Frequent flashbacks make the pacing staccato.	• Trim long flashbacks down to their essential parts. • Identify which flashbacks are key and remove excess. *Evaluation Page:* *Essential Information* *Problem-solving Pages: Cutting a Scene, Merging Scenes*
RESEARCH ISN'T INTEGRATED IN APPROPRIATE PLACES	A part of the story has an issue with believability due to lack of sufficient research.	• Identify areas of the story where more research is needed. • Find relevant information. • Integrate necessary details into the scene. *Genre Page: Historical*
PACING IS TOO FAST	The reader is exhausted, probably confused, and possibly burned out.	• Chart the flow of tension in the story (there should be some variation). • Identify areas where it appears the character has solved a problem before things go wrong again. • Include more narration with character thoughts and reactions. *Evaluation Page: Big Plot Boxes* *Genre Page: Thriller / Horror*

PROBLEM	DESCRIPTION	SOLUTION IDEAS
TENSION AND SUSPENSE AREN'T BUILDING ENOUGH	The story moves forward from event to event with no mounting issues.	• Have problems that the characters don't solve completely. • Make issues compound as the story unfolds. • Relate problems back to main story problem. *Evaluation Page: Big Plot Boxes* *Problem-solving Page: Adding Conflict* *Genre Page: Thriller/Horror*
SAGGY MIDDLE	The story slows in the middle of the book.	• Trim slower scenes. • Check for essential information and cut when necessary. • Evaluate pacing chapter by chapter. • Add more conflict to the storyline. *Evaluation Page: Big Plot Boxes, Essential Information* *Problem-solving Pages: Adding Conflict, Cutting a Scene, Merging Scenes, Adding a Scene, Adding a Subplot, Shifting Story Timeline, Changing a Setting* *Genre Page: Thriller/Horror*

PROBLEM	DESCRIPTION	SOLUTION IDEAS
NOT ENOUGH CONFLICT	The story is a bit slow and not much happens to the characters.	• Identify character's weaknesses and give challenges in line with those weaknesses. • Determine how to integrate a different/new type of conflict. *Evaluation Page: Big Plot Boxes, Cause and Effect* *Problem-solving Pages: Adding Conflict, Adding a Scene, Adding a Subplot, Adding a Character* *Genre Page: Thriller/Horror*
EVENTS FLOW INORGANICALLY	The story bounces from event to event without the events being tied together. One event doesn't logically flow to what happens next in the story.	• Examine the cause and effect relationship between events. • Integrate transitions between events that link them together. • Consider changing the second event if it doesn't make sense on the sequence. *Evaluation Page: Cause and Effect* *Problem-solving Pages: Cutting a Scene, Shifting Story Timeline, Merging Scenes* *Genre Page: Mystery*

PROBLEM	DESCRIPTION	SOLUTION IDEAS
REPEATED EVENTS	The characters do the same thing several times in the story and the reader loses interest.	• Identify which times the event must happen in the story and consider merging or cutting the other times. • Adapt the event by changing the setting, the details, the characters involved, etc. *Problem-solving Pages: Cutting a Scene, Merging Scenes, Changing a Setting*
MUDDLED TIMELINE	It isn't clear when events are taking place or how much time has passed between events.	• Write out the story timeline to address any issues. • Integrate temporal elements such as transition phrases, setting details, clues for the reader. *Planning Page: Updated Story Summary, Updated Story Timeline*

PROBLEM	DESCRIPTION	SOLUTION IDEAS
CHAPTER STRUCTURE IS OFF	The chapter is too short or too long. The chapter cuts off and feels incomplete or drags on and exhausts reader.	• Compare chapter lengths throughout the book. • Evaluate if scenes are completed and if ending of chapter is appropriate. • Shift events into the chapter as appropriate if chapter is too short. • Determine if the long chapter would be better structured as two chapters. *Evaluation Page:* *Chapter Structure*
PROBLEM AND SOLUTION DON'T MATCH	The wrong character solves the problem. The solution doesn't match the problem or doesn't fit well with the story.	• Identify who is the best fit for solving the problem. • Determine a solution directly related to the problem. • Consider multiple solutions that make sense within the context of the story and pick the best fit. *Evaluation Page:* *Problem and Solution*

PROBLEM	DESCRIPTION	SOLUTION IDEAS
CAUSE AND EFFECT DON'T MATCH	The reason behind someone's behavior or why an event happened doesn't relate/explain why it happened. The consequences of a choice or event are not a related result of that choice/event.	• When explaining "why," dig deep and make sure the rationale is related to what happens next. • Examine the results of choices/events and determine if they would logically come from the cause. *Evaluation Page: Cause and Effect*
CHARACTER ACTIONS/CHOICES DON'T MAKE SENSE	The character does something that doesn't align with who they are or what motivates them. The rationale behind actions and choices is unclear, making what they do seem disconnected or off.	• Explore character motivations and ensure they align with character actions. • Include more character thoughts and reflections on actions and choices in the narrative. *Evaluation Page: Problem and Solution, Cause and Effect Problem-solving Page: Fleshing Out Characters*

PROBLEM	DESCRIPTION	SOLUTION IDEAS
PREDICTABLE STORY EVENTS	"I knew it."	• Lessen the amount of foreshadowing if used heavily. • Add in a red herring to throw off the reader. • Write out possible story outcomes, noting which ones would be the most expected, then cross those off. • Adapt the ending as necessary by changing it completely or adding a surprising twist. *Genre Page: Mystery*
OPEN/UNSOLVED SUBPLOTS	Loose ends aren't tied up. The reader never finds out what happens to certain characters.	• Map out subplots and ensure each one is closed up or there's a hint of continuation in another book. • Cut any extra subplots that are loose and don't contribute much to overall plot. *Evaluation Page: Subplot Evaluation* *Problem-solving Page: Adding a Scene, Cutting a Subplot*

PROBLEM	DESCRIPTION	SOLUTION IDEAS
UNSATISFYING ENDING	Oh boy. Lots of things make for an unsatisfying ending: too fast, too easy, unbelievable, someone not getting their just desserts, too cheesy, not enough action, etc.	• Examine the story problem again and the character journey to make sure the climax is a good fit. • Make the climax the absolute worst thing that could happen to the character. • Layer the conflict so multiple things come crashing down at once. • Make sure the right person is solving the problem. • Double check cause and effect as well as problem and solution. • Make sure the resolution completes the character arc and also meets genre norms if applicable. *Evaluation Page: Big Plot, Cause and Effect, Problem and Solution*

PROBLEM	DESCRIPTION	SOLUTION IDEAS
STORY IS TOO LONG/ HAS TOO MANY EVENTS	You're wayyyy over word count norms for your genre. Time to slice and dice.	• Do an in-depth look at your story timeline and identify which events are absolutely crucial to the main story problem and what can be cut. • Cut out nonessential information at every level: chapter, scene, paragraph, sentence. *Evaluation Page: Essential Information Problem-solving Pages: Cutting a Subplot, Cutting a Scene, Merging Scenes, Cutting a Character*
STORY IS TOO SHORT/ DOESN'T HAVE ENOUGH EVENTS	You're not anywhere near the word count norms for your genre.	• Consider adding a subplot or two. • Expand on character development. • Find places to add more conflict. *Problem-solving Pages: Adding a Subplot, Adding a Scene, Adding a Character, Fleshing Out Characters, Adding Conflict*

COMMON PROBLEM & SOLUTION IDEAS

SETTING

PROBLEM	DESCRIPTION	SOLUTION IDEAS
SETTING MISSING FROM SCENES	Dialogue and characters seem to be floating in space.	• Determine where exactly scene is occurring. • Integrate setting details and use different sensory elements. • Show the characters interacting with the setting. *Evaluation Page: Setting*
NOT ENOUGH SETTING DETAILS	The setting is present but pretty bare.	• Expand the setting using different sensory elements. • Include key details that show the feeling of the setting. • Show the characters interacting with the setting. *Evaluation Page: Setting*
TOO MANY SETTING DETAILS	We know every single item in that room and where it came from.	• Cut details down into what lays the groundwork, what characters interact with, and what shows the feeling of the setting. *Evaluation Page: Essential Information*

PROBLEM	DESCRIPTION	SOLUTION IDEAS
FLAT/BORING SETTING	A standard office, the usual park, an average living room.	• Integrate key details into the setting, particularly ones that demonstrate the character of whoever lives/works/interacts in that space. • Include something interesting or unusual but believable. *Problem-solving Page:* *Changing a Setting*
REPETITIVE SETTINGS	Is this the fifth time they've been to the same restaurant?	• Cut or merge scenes that occur in the same setting over and over. • Change the setting for a few of the scenes. • Make small changes in the setting each time such as the weather, how tidy it is, the time of day, etc. *Problem-solving Page:* *Merging Scenes*

PROBLEM	DESCRIPTION	SOLUTION IDEAS
CONFUSING WORLDBUILDING (FANTASY/SCI-FI)	The reader doesn't have a good grip on the fictional world where the story takes place.	• Draw maps of created lands. • Write out relevant background info such as native creatures, modes of transportation, home styles...things a visitor would see and hear as they traveled through this land. • Include relevant details as the reader needs them in the story. *Genre Page:* *Fantasy Worldbuilding*

COMMON PROBLEM & SOLUTION IDEAS

LANGUAGE

PROBLEM	DESCRIPTION	SOLUTION IDEAS
WEAK FIRST LINE/ LAST LINE	Your opening line doesn't grab the attention of the reader. Your closing line doesn't work well.	• Research your favorite openers and closers in your favorite books. • Make a list of many possible openers and closers. • Put your opening and closing lines together and see how they fit.
CLUTTERED PROSE	Sentences are bulky and don't flow smoothly.	See Editing Checklist.
TENSE JUMPS	The tense goes back and forth between past and present (not including flashbacks).	• Print your chapter and highlight your verbs. • Change any that are not in the main tense.
WEAK ACTION LANGUAGE	Your sentences are clunky and don't read in an exciting way.	• Break apart and shorten longer paragraphs in your action scene. • Shorten your sentences. • Choose specific verbs that portray action. • Make character thoughts quick.

PROBLEM	DESCRIPTION	SOLUTION IDEAS
DIALOGUE IS INORGANIC	Characters don't sound realistic.	• Each character should have a flavor to how they speak that differentiates them whether it be an accent, word choice, syntax, sentence length, favored phrases, cursing, etc. • Use contractions to make it sound more like speaking. • Check for clichés and stereotypical phrases. • Pretend you have to pay a nickel for every word of dialogue so every word counts, no excess. • Skip greetings/routine conversation as much as possible. • Cut out repeated reconveying of events in dialogue. *Evaluation Page:* *Essential Information* *See Editing Checklist* *Problem-solving Page:* *Language Use*

PROBLEM	DESCRIPTION	SOLUTION IDEAS
TELLING INSTEAD OF SHOWING	The reader is told what happens instead of shown— they don't experience the event.	• Use descriptive language to convey the message. • Break down the event into smaller pieces and include character thoughts and reactions. • Don't directly state feelings, show the effects of them, such as physical reactions. *Problem-solving Page: Language Use*
NARRATIVE DISTANCE	The reader doesn't feel close to the character.	• Tighten the POV by adding more narration through their perspective. (Try rewriting the scene in first person and seeing what details you added, then redo it again in third.) • Include more character thoughts and reactions. • Remove sense words (Look, see, noticed, heard, etc.) and only state what was sensed as story facts. *Problem-solving Page: Language Use, Fleshing Out a Character*

PROBLEM	DESCRIPTION	SOLUTION IDEAS
NARRATIVE BALANCE IS OFF	There is more dialogue than narration. There is more narration than dialogue.	• Determine which parts are imbalanced. • Evaluate if narration/ dialogue should be added or removed to create a better balance. *Problem-solving Page: Language Use*
VOICE IS FLAT	The story lacks the flavor of the author.	• Find appropriate places to integrate humor. • Use your own descriptive language including similes and metaphors. • Write in your own style, don't attempt to imitate others.

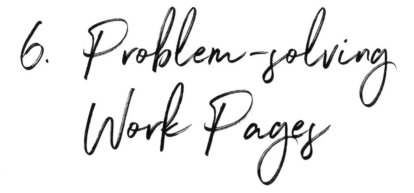

6. Problem-solving Work Pages

FLESHING OUT CHARACTERS

Character: Physical Description:

Background:

Motivation/Goal:

CHARACTER

FLESHING OUT CHARACTERS

Strengths:

Weaknesses:

Vulnerabilities:

What drives them?

What annoys them?

CHARACTER

FLESHING OUT CHARACTERS

How do they react when they are: sad, angry, happy, other?

Are they pessimistic or optimistic?

Unique characteristics:

Hobbies:

Gestures/Physical habits:

CHARACTER

FLESHING OUT CHARACTERS

Favorite words or phrases:

Best thing that could happen to them:

Worst thing that could happen to them:

Other information:

CHARACTER

ADDING A CHARACTER

Character:

Backstory:

Physical Description:

Motivation:

CHARACTER

ADDING A CHARACTER

Relationship to Other Characters:

Places to Add Character into Scene:

Places to Reference Character (not in scene):

CHARACTER

CUTTING A CHARACTER

Character:

Places in Story Timeline Where They Appear:

Contributions to the Story that Need to be Shifted to Other Characters:

Other Characters Who Will Now Give These Story Contributions:

Where in Story Timeline Other Characters Will Give Contributions:

CHARACTER

MERGING CHARACTERS

Characters to be Merged:

New Single Identity:

Physical Description:

Background Info:

Places Where Original Characters Appear:

Places Where New Single Identity Needs to Be:

CHARACTER

CHANGING A CHARACTER

Character:

New Change:

Effects on Thoughts/Reactions:

Effects on Actions:

Other Effects (appearance, skills, where they live, etc.):

Places Where Character Appears that Need Revision:

CHARACTER

CLEARING UP POV

Chapter or Scene:

Which character is the best fit for the reader to experience the scene through? (Consider who is doing the action, who has the knowledge, who will have the biggest emotional response.)

How will they react emotionally during the scene?

What thoughts will they have during the scene?

What is their feeling towards the setting?

AN EXERCISE: *Rewrite the scene in first person and see what other information or details you add. Now do the scene again in third person and include those details.*

CHARACTER

ADDING A SUBPLOT

Subplot:

Characters Involved:

Subplot Setting(s):

Details:

Places to Add Subplot to Story Timeline:

Other Scenes/Subplots Affected:

PLOT

CUTTING A SUBPLOT

Subplot:

Locations(s) in Story Timeline:

Key Information Being Cut:

New Location for Key Information:

Other Scenes Where Subplot is Mentioned that Need to be Revised:

PLOT

ADDING A SCENE

Scene to Add:

Location in Story Timeline:

Scene Events/Details:

Other Places to Reference this Scene:

PACING CHECK: *Does the pacing still work with this additional scene?*

PLOT

CUTTING A SCENE

Scene to Cut:

Location in Story Timeline:

Information in Scene to be Moved Elsewhere:

New Home for this Info:

Other Places that Reference this Scene and Need Revision:

PACING CHECK: *Does the pacing still work without this scene?*

PLOT

MERGING SCENES

Scenes to be Merged:

Location(s) in Story Timeline:

Parts to Cut:

Parts to Keep:

PACING CHECK: *Does the new merged scene flow well with the story pacing?*

PLOT

SHIFTING STORY TIMELINE/MOVING SCENES

Original Timeline:

New Timeline:

Changes to be Made Before New Shift:

Changes to be Made After New Shift:

PACING CHECK: *Does the new timeline keep the appropriate story pace?*

PLOT

CLEANING UP/CLARIFYING BACKSTORY

Character:

Backstory Details:

Impact on Character Thoughts/Choices:

Places to Integrate Backstory:

PLOT

ADDING CONFLICT

Chapter/Scene:

Current Conflict: Internal or External?

Conflict Ideas for Battling SELF:
(memories, bad habits, self-criticism, fear, doubt, personal expectations)

Conflict Ideas for Battling OTHERS:
(attacker, judgmental/critical person, competitive person)

PLOT

ADDING CONFLICT

Conflict Ideas for Battling NATURE:

(weather, time, animals, natural disasters, pollution, disease)

Conflict Ideas for Battling MACHINE:

(AI, computer virus, broken/malfunctioning equipment, cell phones)

Conflict Ideas for Battling SUPERNATURAL:

(God/faith, deities, mythical creatures, ghosts, evil forces)

PLOT

ADDING CONFLICT

Conflict Ideas for Battling FATE:

(premonitions, mystics, predetermined paths, genetic destinies)

What conflict ideas can you layer or combine to create a crisis? Include internal and external.

**Good conflict is in direct opposition to the character's goals
and motivations and plays on their weaknesses.**

PLOT

CHANGING A SETTING

Current Setting:

Updated Setting:

Details:

Scenes that Take Place in New Setting:

How New Setting Affects Characters:

How New Setting Affects Events:

SETTING

LANGUAGE USE

Repeated Words/Crutch Words:

Places to Improve Language: (Check as many as necessary.)

CHARACTER/SCENE	DESCRIPTION	DIALOGUE	CHARACTER THOUGHTS	CLUTTERED PROSE	ACTION LANGUAGE	GENERAL NARRATION

LANGUAGE

EDITING CHECKLIST FOR CLEANING UP PROSE

CONSIDER EDITING	EXAMPLES
PASSIVE VERBS	Was, were, is, are
SENSE WORDS	Look, notice, saw, heard, smell
ADVERBS	Quickly, angrily
WEAK VERBS	Walked, set down
WAS + GERUND	Was running (ran)
VERB + IN FEELING	Yelled in exasperation
THAT	I knew that he went...
JUST	She just wanted...
VERY	He was very upset.
FELT	She felt sad.
SUDDENLY	Suddenly the door shut.
ACTION "AS"	He yelled as he jumped...
BEGAN TO/BEGINNING TO	She began to open the door...

LANGUAGE

CONSIDER EDITING	EXAMPLES
UNAWARE POV SLIPS	She didn't notice... He didn't realize...
PATTERN OF SENTENCE BEGINNINGS	She this...She that.... She this...She that...
TOO MANY PAST PERFECT "HAD"	She had gone and had seen, and had decided...
GREETINGS IN DIALOGUE	Hello, good morning, how are you?
SPEAKER TAGS	Use mostly "said"
NON-CONTRACTIONS IN DIALOGUE	"She is not here." "I am hot."
OVERUSE OF CHARACTER NAME	*Use pronouns as much as possible
SENTENCE LENGTHS	*Check for a variety in sentence length and structure
STRINGS OF PREPOSITIONS	By the river near the bluff over the mountain...
MULTIPLE ADJECTIVES	The dainty, elegant flower in the blue speckled shiny pot.
EXCLAMATION POINTS	*Limit to as few as possible
LONG PARAGRAPHS	*Break up as appropriate

LANGUAGE

7. Genre Work Pages

CHANGE IN MAGIC/TECHNOLOGY

Current Magic/Technology:

New Change:

Effect on Characters:

FANTASY/SCI-FI

CHANGE IN MAGIC/TECHNOLOGY

Effect on Events:

Effect on Setting:

Places in Story Timeline to Update:

FANTASY/SCI-FI

INTEGRATING WORLDBUILDING

WORLDBUILDING INFO	WHERE TO INTRODUCE INFO

FANTASY/SCI-FI

CHARACTER RELATIONSHIPS

Characters in Potential Relationship:

Reasons Not to be Together – Character 1:

Reasons Not to be Together – Character 2:

Reasons to be Together – Character 1:

ROMANCE

CHARACTER RELATIONSHIPS

Reasons to be Together – Character 2:

Events that Pull Characters Apart:

Events that Draw Characters Together:

ROMANCE

INTEGRATING RESEARCH

Historical Element:

Research Details:

Effects on Characters/Events:

Places to be Integrated:

HISTORICAL

TENSION GROWTH

Scene: _____ Suspense Level: (circle) 1 2 3 4 5

Scene: _____ Suspense Level: (circle) 1 2 3 4 5

Scene: _____ Suspense Level: (circle) 1 2 3 4 5

Scene: _____ Suspense Level: (circle) 1 2 3 4 5

Scene: _____ Suspense Level: (circle) 1 2 3 4 5

Scene: _____ Suspense Level: (circle) 1 2 3 4 5

Scene: _____ Suspense Level: (circle) 1 2 3 4 5

Remember, some downtime for the reader to process is normal,
just not several slower scenes in a row.

THRILLER/HORROR

FORESHADOWING/READER CLUES

Clue to be Included:

Character Giving Clue:

Location in Story Timeline:

Other Scenes to Mention Clue:

MYSTERY

FORESHADOWING/READER CLUES

Clue to be Included:

Character Giving Clue:

Location in Story Timeline:

Other Scenes to Mention Clue:

MYSTERY

8. Getting & Managing Feedback

Feedback is essential for any story to become a success. It's impossible for the author to perceive every issue in their work and fix it alone. We can't always see the problems and we are also a bit protective of our babies. That's where other people come in. They can help us pinpoint issues and suggest possible fixes. It's ultimately up to the writer to decide what to do but having the information guides us in the right direction.

Types of Feedback

Critique Partners: These are the first people who should see your work. Primarily because they are fellow writers and have insider knowledge. Having the first set of eyes be from a writer is imperative. You don't want someone who doesn't understand the craft of writing to give you inaccurate, dare I say, bad advice. Writers will be specific in their feedback because they recognize character arcs, narrative structure, and common issues in writing. Someone who reads a lot, your grandma, or your dog doesn't have the knowledge a fellow writer does.

Finding reliable critique partners can take some work. The best way is to get involved in your local writing community and find out if there is a local group. If not, you'll have to network with fellow writers and ask around to see who is looking for a critique partner. Critiquing an entire manuscript takes a lot of time and effort. You will probably have to pay it forward with several other writers before asking to have yours critiqued. Some writers make better critique partners than others. You'll have to test out who is a good match for your genre and style and who has a good eye for spotting issues and coming up with solution ideas.

When are you ready for a critique? After you've been through several rounds of revision and have addressed all of your big and medium issues, in addition to some smaller ones. It's okay if your story isn't perfectly polished since you'll be making changes to it after getting feedback.

Professional Editors:

There are several different types of professional editors, but the main two are content editors and copy editors, although most do both. Content editing addresses the narrative content of your story. An editor can point out things like slow pacing, unclear character motivations, issues with story problems and so on. They provide a *professional* critique. Copy editing focuses on the nuts and bolts of the writing and edits for mechanics, grammar, and word usage. This is when your work is polished up.

Professional editing is a necessary expense to get your project ready for the world. Research editing rates beforehand so you aren't surprised by the price tag. You're paying for a professional to spend a significant amount of time with your work. When looking for an editor, be sure to check their credentials and experience in the industry. Just like with critique partners, you'll find some editors a better fit than others.

Content editing is best done after you've worked with critique partners and have already cleaned up the manuscript a bit. Copy editing should be done after all content issues, big, medium, and small, are addressed and the story is ready to go.

Beta Readers:

These are your first test audience since they are a writer's favorite...readers! Reader impressions are important because they give you feedback on characters and parts of the story they liked and didn't like. It's important to have beta readers that read books within your genre. You don't want someone who only reads biographies to give you feedback about your fantasy story. Anyone can read books. You want an informed opinion, not a generic one that may not be aligned with genre norms.

Look among your friends, neighbors, and contacts and find out who is an avid reader in your genre. Avoid having family members as beta readers. They can be biased about your work, and in a more favorable direction. Honesty helps your work become better, not a pat on the back.

Beta readers can be used at different times during the finalization process after content issues have been addressed. You can use them before or after hiring an editor. Just remember, a person only gets one fresh read, so be judicious when you ask for beta readers.

Managing Feedback

Getting feedback on your work isn't easy. It's like being told you have an ugly baby. All you want to do is tell the other person they are wrong and punch them in the face. Your baby is perfect, thank you very much. But alas, our babies are not perfect and punching other people doesn't make your story better, unfortunately.

There is one thing you can always anticipate when you receive feedback: it will cause an emotional response. You may start out angry, particularly at the idiot jerk who doesn't know anything about anything. For me, the angrier I am, the more likely the person is right. I just don't want to face the reality of how much work it will be to fix it. Then the anger can shift into sadness and insecurity where you think your story sucks and ultimately, you suck. Spend some time working through these emotions and know that they are normal. You don't suck. Your story needs work, just like everyone else's. No one ever writes a perfect story with absolutely no problems whatsoever.

Once you've gotten through the emotional roller coaster, you also need to give yourself time to digest and evaluate the feedback. All of these are opinions, some more reliable than others. You ultimately get to decide what to do with your work and what is best for your story. Remember always to thank the person, even if you disagree with their feedback. It takes a significant amount of time to critique or beta read a book and you should always be appreciative, especially if you ever want them to do it again.

The following pages are to help you obtain and evaluate feedback:

- Beta Reader Guide Sheet
- Reviewing Critiques/Beta Reader Feedback
- Reviewing Content Edits
- Reviewing Copy Edits

Please Provide Feedback for the Following

CHARACTER

READER: _____

Character 1 Name:

Likable/Unlikable as Appropriate	1	2	3	4	5
Relatable	1	2	3	4	5
Realistic	1	2	3	4	5

Comments on Above:

Other Comments for this Character:

FEEDBACK

Character 2 Name:

Likable/Unlikable as Appropriate	1	2	3	4	5
Relatable	1	2	3	4	5
Realistic	1	2	3	4	5

Comments on Above:

Other Comments for this Character:

FEEDBACK

Please Provide Feedback for the Following

> ## PLOT

Did the opening scene grab your attention and make you want to read more?

Which story events did you enjoy?

Which story events were confusing?

FEEDBACK

Were there any slow or boring parts?

Was there enough excitement in the climax?

Did you feel satisfied with the ending?

FEEDBACK

Please Provide Feedback for the Following

SETTING

Setting 1:

Setting Details   1   2   3   4   5
Feel Immersed in Setting   1   2   3   4   5

Comments on Above:

Any Setting Inconsistencies?

Other Comments for this Setting:

FEEDBACK

Setting 2:

Setting Details	1	2	3	4	5
Feel Immersed in Setting	1	2	3	4	5

Comments on Above:

Any Setting Inconsistencies?

Other Comments for this Setting:

FEEDBACK

Please Provide Feedback for the Following

LANGUAGE

Frequently Used Words or Phrases:

Confusing Words or Phrases (please include page number):

Thank you so much for your time and effort in giving me feedback.

I appreciate your honesty and all your help with this project!

FEEDBACK

REVIEWING CONTENT EDITS

Big Issues: Solution Ideas:

Medium Issues: Solution Ideas:

Small Issues: Solution Ideas:

FEEDBACK

REVIEWING CONTENT EDITS

WHAT I DISAGREE WITH	REASON	EMOTIONAL RESPONSE OR WHAT'S BEST FOR STORY?	NEED A SECOND OPINION?

FEEDBACK

REVIEWING COPY EDITS

New Things Learned Upon Review:

My Bad Habits:

FEEDBACK

REVIEWING CRITIQUES/BETA READER FEEDBACK

Reviewer:

Reliability Rating   1   2   3   4   5

Key Feedback:

Plan to Address Issue(s):

FEEDBACK

9. Resource Recommendations

TOPIC	RESOURCES
CHARACTER:	
CREATING CHARACTERS	• *Characters and Viewpoint* by Orson Scott Card • *Creating Characters* by Steven James • *Characters, Emotion, and Viewpoint* by Nancy Kress • *The Negative Trait Thesaurus* by A. Ackerman and Becca Puglisi • *The Positive Trait Thesaurus* by A. Ackerman and Becca Puglisi • *GMC: Goal, Motivation and Conflict* by Debra Dixon
ANTAGONISTS	• *13 Steps to Evil: How to Craft Superbad Villains* by Sacha Black
CHARACTER EMOTIONS	• *The Emotion Thesaurus* by Angela Ackerman and Becca Puglisi • *Characters, Emotion, and Viewpoint* by Nancy Kress • *Creating Character Emotions* by Ann Hood

TOPIC	RESOURCES
CHARACTER ARC	• *Creating Character Arcs* by K.M. Weiland • *Creating Character Arcs Workbook* by K.M. Weiland
POV	• *Characters and Viewpoint* by Orson Scott Card • *Characters, Emotion, and Viewpoint* by Nancy Kress • *Deep Point of View* by Marcy Kennedy
RELATIONSHIP DEVELOPMENT	• *Romancing the Beat* by Gwen Hayes
CHARACTER NAMES	• *Master Lists for Writers* by Bryn Donovan
PLOT:	
PLOT IN GENERAL	• *Plot and Structure* by James Scott Bell • *How to Write a Novel Using the Snowflake Method* by Randy Ingermanson • *20 Master Plots and How to Build Them* by Ronald Tobias
OPENINGS	• *Wired for Story: The Writer's Guide to Using Brain Science to Hook Readers from the Very First Sentence* by Lisa Cron

TOPIC	RESOURCES
TENSION AND SUSPENSE	• *Mastering Suspense, Structure, and Plot* by J. Cleland and H. Ephron • *Elements of Fiction Writing – Conflict and Suspense* by James Scott Bell
CONFLICT	• *Elements of Fiction Writing – Conflict and Suspense* by James Scott Bell • *Writing with Emotion, Tension, and Conflict* by Cheryl St. John
SCENES	• *Writing Deep Scenes* by Martha Alderson and Jordan Rosenfeld • *Structuring Your Novel* by K.M. Weiland • *Scene and Structure* by Jack M. Bickham • *Plot Perfect: How to Build Unforgettable Stories Scene by Scene* by Paula Munier • *Writing Fight Scenes* by Rayne Hall • *Writing Scary Scenes* by Rayne Hall
SETTING:	
SETTINGS	• *Write Great Fiction – Description and Setting* by Ron Rozelle • *The Urban Setting Thesaurus* by A. Ackerman and B. Puglisi • *The Rural Setting Thesaurus* by A. Ackerman and B. Puglisi • *Writing Vivid Settings* by Rayne Hall • *Writing Active Settings Books* by Mary Buckham
WORLDBUILDING	• *How to Write Science Fiction and Fantasy* by Orson Scott Card

TOPIC	RESOURCES
LANGUAGE:	
DIALOGUE	• *How to Write Dazzling Dialogue* by James Scott Bell • *Writing Vivid Dialogue* by Rayne Hall
SHOW VS. TELL	• *Show Don't Tell* by Sandra Gerth • *Understanding Show Don't Tell* by Janice Hardy
VOICE	• *Voice: The Secret Power of Writing* by James Scott Bell
USAGE	• *The Elements of Style* by William Strunk Jr. and E.B. White
INSPIRATION/MINDSET:	• *Big Magic* by Elizabeth Gilbert • *On Writing* by Stephen King

10. Planning Work Pages

REREADING REVIEW NOTES

Chapter:

Revision Notes for this Chapter:

Revision Notes for More than this Chapter:

REREADING REVIEW NOTES

Chapter:

Revision Notes for this Chapter:

Revision Notes for More than this Chapter:

REREADING REVIEW NOTES

Chapter:

Revision Notes for this Chapter:

Revision Notes for More than this Chapter:

REREADING REVIEW NOTES

Chapter:

Revision Notes for this Chapter:

Revision Notes for More than this Chapter:

REREADING REVIEW NOTES

Chapter:

Revision Notes for this Chapter:

Revision Notes for More than this Chapter:

REREADING REVIEW NOTES

Chapter:

Revision Notes for this Chapter:

Revision Notes for More than this Chapter:

REREADING REVIEW NOTES

Chapter:

Revision Notes for this Chapter:

Revision Notes for More than this Chapter:

REREADING REVIEW NOTES

Chapter:

Revision Notes for this Chapter:

Revision Notes for More than this Chapter:

REREADING REVIEW NOTES

Chapter:

Revision Notes for this Chapter:

Revision Notes for More than this Chapter:

REREADING REVIEW NOTES

Chapter:

Revision Notes for this Chapter:

Revision Notes for More than this Chapter:

REREADING REVIEW NOTES

Chapter:

Revision Notes for this Chapter:

Revision Notes for More than this Chapter:

REREADING REVIEW NOTES

Chapter:

Revision Notes for this Chapter:

Revision Notes for More than this Chapter:

REREADING REVIEW NOTES

Chapter:

Revision Notes for this Chapter:

Revision Notes for More than this Chapter:

REREADING REVIEW NOTES

Chapter:

Revision Notes for this Chapter:

Revision Notes for More than this Chapter:

REREADING REVIEW NOTES

Chapter:

Revision Notes for this Chapter:

Revision Notes for More than this Chapter:

REREADING REVIEW NOTES

Chapter:

Revision Notes for this Chapter:

Revision Notes for More than this Chapter:

REREADING REVIEW NOTES

Chapter:

Revision Notes for this Chapter:

Revision Notes for More than this Chapter:

REREADING REVIEW NOTES

Chapter:

Revision Notes for this Chapter:

Revision Notes for More than this Chapter:

REREADING REVIEW NOTES

Chapter:

Revision Notes for this Chapter:

Revision Notes for More than this Chapter:

REREADING REVIEW NOTES

Chapter:

Revision Notes for this Chapter:

Revision Notes for More than this Chapter:

REREADING REVIEW NOTES

Chapter:

Revision Notes for this Chapter:

Revision Notes for More than this Chapter:

REREADING REVIEW NOTES

Chapter:

Revision Notes for this Chapter:

Revision Notes for More than this Chapter:

REREADING REVIEW NOTES

Chapter:

Revision Notes for this Chapter:

Revision Notes for More than this Chapter:

REREADING REVIEW NOTES

Chapter:

Revision Notes for this Chapter:

Revision Notes for More than this Chapter:

REREADING REVIEW NOTES

Chapter:

Revision Notes for this Chapter:

Revision Notes for More than this Chapter:

REREADING REVIEW NOTES

Chapter:

Revision Notes for this Chapter:

Revision Notes for More than this Chapter:

REREADING REVIEW NOTES

Chapter:

Revision Notes for this Chapter:

Revision Notes for More than this Chapter:

REREADING REVIEW NOTES

Chapter:

Revision Notes for this Chapter:

Revision Notes for More than this Chapter:

REREADING REVIEW NOTES

Chapter:

Revision Notes for this Chapter:

Revision Notes for More than this Chapter:

REREADING REVIEW NOTES

Chapter:

Revision Notes for this Chapter:

Revision Notes for More than this Chapter:

REREADING REVIEW NOTES

Chapter:

Revision Notes for this Chapter:

Revision Notes for More than this Chapter:

PRIORITIZING ISSUES

Big Issues: (overall plot/across chapters/significant time to fix)   *ADDRESS FIRST*

Medium Issues: (chapter or scene level/modest time to fix)   *ADDRESS NEXT*

PLOT

PRIORITIZING ISSUES

Small Issues: (paragraph or sentence level / quicker fixes)   *ADDRESS LAST*

Notes:

PLOT

ORIGINAL STORY SUMMARY

CHAPTER	SCENE	EVENTS	POV	DAY/TIME

PLOT

UPDATED STORY SUMMARY

CHAPTER	SCENE	EVENTS	POV	DAY/TIME

PLOT

ORIGINAL STORY TIMELINE

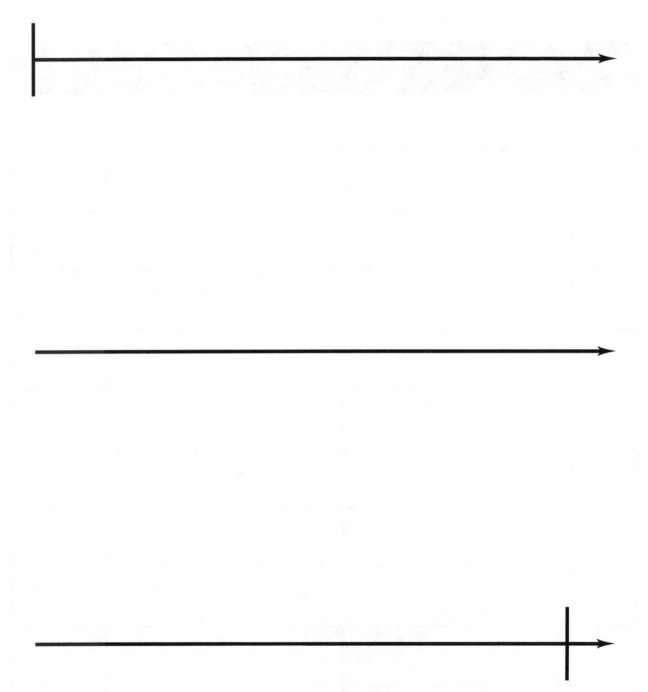

PLOT

UPDATED STORY TIMELINE

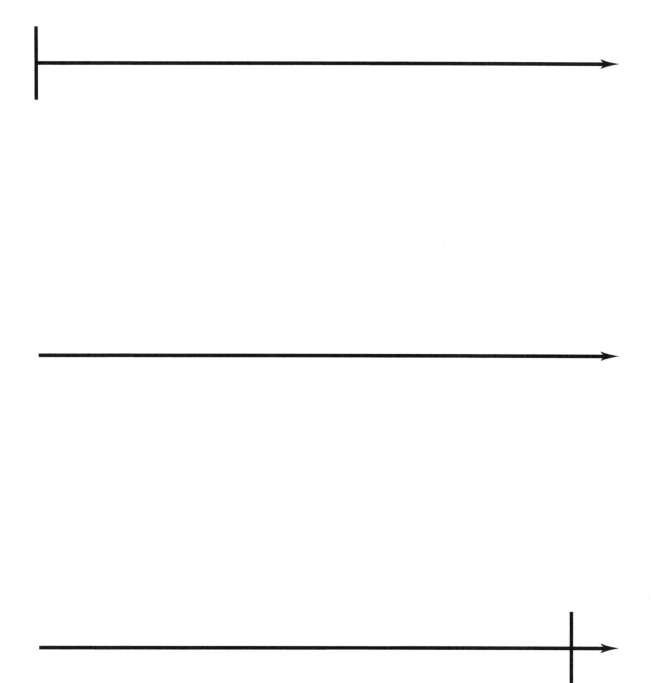

PLOT

REVISION PLAN

Chapter:

What to Clean Up: (Prioritize in order of big issues to small issues for all parts.)

What to Remove:

What to Add:

Other Revisions:

REVISION PLAN

Chapter:

What to Clean Up: (Prioritize in order of big issues to small issues for all parts.)

What to Remove:

What to Add:

Other Revisions:

REVISION PLAN

Chapter:

What to Clean Up: (Prioritize in order of big issues to small issues for all parts.)

What to Remove:

What to Add:

Other Revisions:

REVISION PLAN

Chapter:

What to Clean Up: (Prioritize in order of big issues to small issues for all parts.)

What to Remove:

What to Add:

Other Revisions:

REVISION PLAN

Chapter:

What to Clean Up: (Prioritize in order of big issues to small issues for all parts.)

What to Remove:

What to Add:

Other Revisions:

REVISION PLAN

Chapter:

What to Clean Up: (Prioritize in order of big issues to small issues for all parts.)

What to Remove:

What to Add:

Other Revisions:

REVISION PLAN

Chapter:

What to Clean Up: (Prioritize in order of big issues to small issues for all parts.)

What to Remove:

What to Add:

Other Revisions:

REVISION PLAN

Chapter:

What to Clean Up: (Prioritize in order of big issues to small issues for all parts.)

What to Remove:

What to Add:

Other Revisions:

REVISION PLAN

Chapter:

What to Clean Up: (Prioritize in order of big issues to small issues for all parts.)

What to Remove:

What to Add:

Other Revisions:

REVISION PLAN

Chapter:

What to Clean Up: (Prioritize in order of big issues to small issues for all parts.)

What to Remove:

What to Add:

Other Revisions:

REVISION PLAN

Chapter:

What to Clean Up: (Prioritize in order of big issues to small issues for all parts.)

What to Remove:

What to Add:

Other Revisions:

REVISION PLAN

Chapter:

What to Clean Up: (Prioritize in order of big issues to small issues for all parts.)

What to Remove:

What to Add:

Other Revisions:

REVISION PLAN

Chapter:

What to Clean Up: (Prioritize in order of big issues to small issues for all parts.)

What to Remove:

What to Add:

Other Revisions:

REVISION PLAN

Chapter:

What to Clean Up: (Prioritize in order of big issues to small issues for all parts.)

What to Remove:

What to Add:

Other Revisions:

REVISION PLAN

Chapter:

What to Clean Up: (Prioritize in order of big issues to small issues for all parts.)

What to Remove:

What to Add:

Other Revisions:

REVISION PLAN

Chapter:

What to Clean Up: (Prioritize in order of big issues to small issues for all parts.)

What to Remove:

What to Add:

Other Revisions:

REVISION PLAN

Chapter:

What to Clean Up: (Prioritize in order of big issues to small issues for all parts.)

What to Remove:

What to Add:

Other Revisions:

REVISION PLAN

Chapter:

What to Clean Up: (Prioritize in order of big issues to small issues for all parts.)

What to Remove:

What to Add:

Other Revisions:

REVISION PLAN

Chapter:

What to Clean Up: (Prioritize in order of big issues to small issues for all parts.)

What to Remove:

What to Add:

Other Revisions:

REVISION PLAN

Chapter:

What to Clean Up: (Prioritize in order of big issues to small issues for all parts.)

What to Remove:

What to Add:

Other Revisions:

REVISION PLAN

Chapter:

What to Clean Up: (Prioritize in order of big issues to small issues for all parts.)

What to Remove:

What to Add:

Other Revisions:

REVISION PLAN

Chapter:

What to Clean Up: (Prioritize in order of big issues to small issues for all parts.)

What to Remove:

What to Add:

Other Revisions:

REVISION PLAN

Chapter:

What to Clean Up: (Prioritize in order of big issues to small issues for all parts.)

What to Remove:

What to Add:

Other Revisions:

REVISION PLAN

Chapter:

What to Clean Up: (Prioritize in order of big issues to small issues for all parts.)

What to Remove:

What to Add:

Other Revisions:

About Writer's Atelier

The mission of Writer's Atelier is to encourage writers to have the confidence to believe in their writing while they also work to improve it. At conception, Writer's Atelier was solely an editorial company started by Writer and Editor, Racquel Henry. After many years of helping writers improve their writing by way of paper, Racquel realized she wanted to transcend that experience into a more tangible space. Writer's Atelier is now a physical and online place writers can visit to associate or network with other writers and perfect their craft. The Writer's Atelier facility is a space where literary groups can gather, attend writing workshops, and feel a sense of community. Above all, Writer's Atelier is a safe space.

Find out more about our studio via our website: www.writersatelier.com.

We love hearing from writers who have found our materials helpful! If you liked *The Complete Revision Workbook for Writers*, please consider leaving us a review on Goodreads or Amazon. Spreading the love on social networks is also very much appreciated! Be sure to tag us and our authors! Find us on Instagram, Facebook, and Twitter: @WritersAtelier.

More books from Writer's Atelier:

The Writer's Atelier Little Book of Writing Affirmations by Racquel Henry (2018)

Binge Write Your Novel Workbook by Kerry Evelyn (Summer 2019)

About the Author

Previously an elementary teacher, Arielle Haughee (Hoy) is a three-time RP-LA-winning multi-genre author and the owner of Orange Blossom Publishing. She is the Contest Coordinator and a writing coach at Writer's Atelier writing studio, as well as a judge for the Royal Palm Literary Awards. Arielle is the author of *The Complete Revision Workbook for Writers* as well as the picture books *Grumbler* and *Joyride* (2019) and the editor of the *How I Met My Other* anthology series. Learn more about Arielle at www.ariellehaughee.com or follow her on Facebook or Instagram @orange_blossom_books.

CPSIA information can be obtained
at www.ICGtesting.com
Printed in the USA
BVHW012006250319
543652BV00005B/10/P